Color and Play Instructions:

1. Find a Color and Play page in your coloring book and color the picture.

2. Download the FREE Disney Color and Play App on your mobile device and follow the instructions to create a magical 3D version of your coloring masterpiece in this book!

3. Using the Color and Play App, hold your device over the picture until you see the ★✪★ in the corners.

Watch your picture come to life!

You'll find extra Color and Play pages to encourage creativity. Color your favorite characters in different ways for hours of magical play!

A virtual version of specially marked coloring pages may also be purchased separately as an in-app purchase. If you have already purchased the virtual coloring pages, this book will not unlock any additional content.

bendon

The BENDON name, logo and Tear and Share are trademarks of Bendon, Inc., Ashland, OH 44805.

WATCH YOUR PICTURE COME TO LIFE!

HOLD YOUR DEVICE OVER THE PICTURE UNTIL YOU SEE THE ★ IN THE CORNERS.

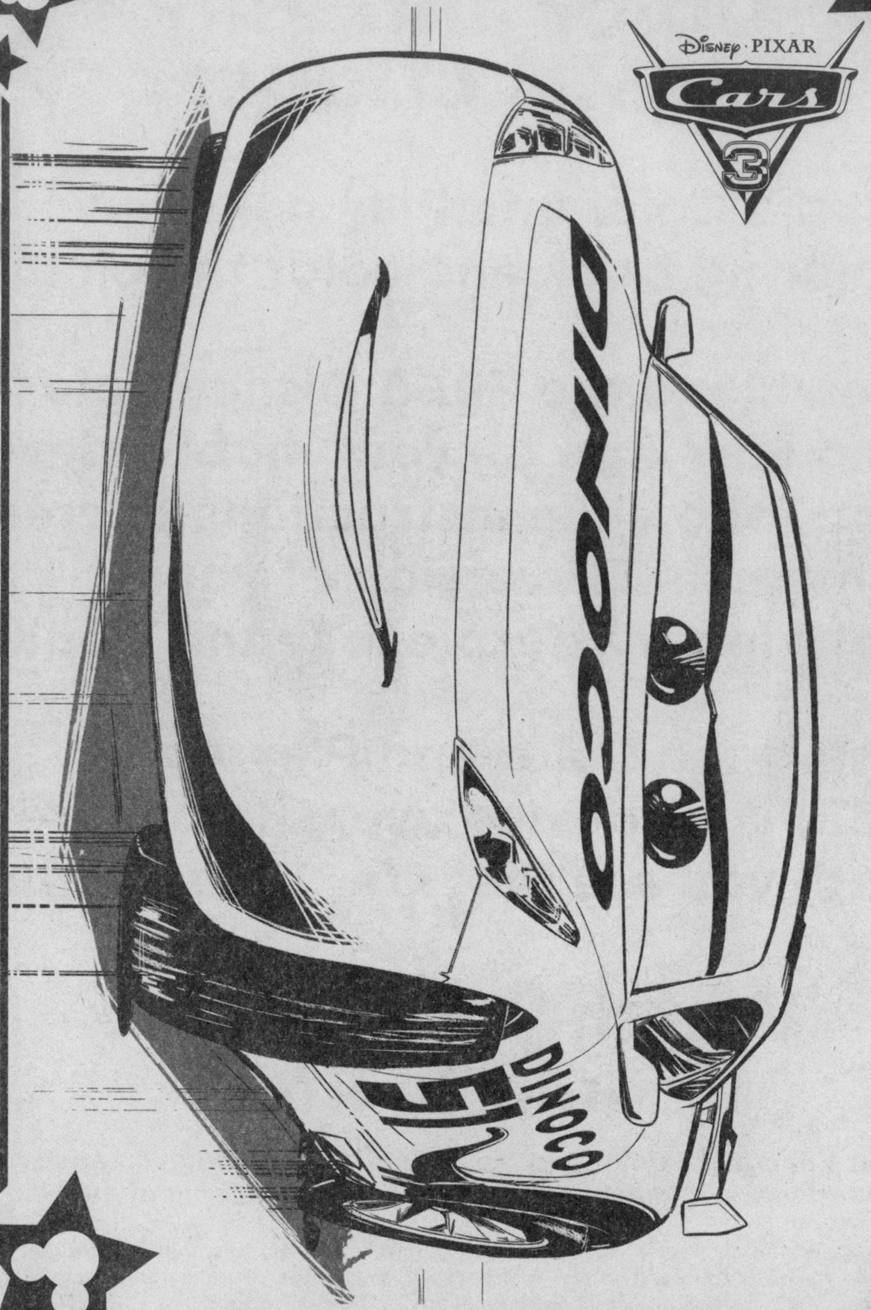

Disney · PIXAR Cars 3

DINOCO

DINOCO

Cruz Ramirez is the new Dinoco Race Car.

WATCH YOUR PICTURE COME TO LIFE!

HOLD YOUR DEVICE OVER THE PICTURE UNTIL YOU SEE THE ★ IN THE CORNERS.

Disney · PIXAR Cars 3

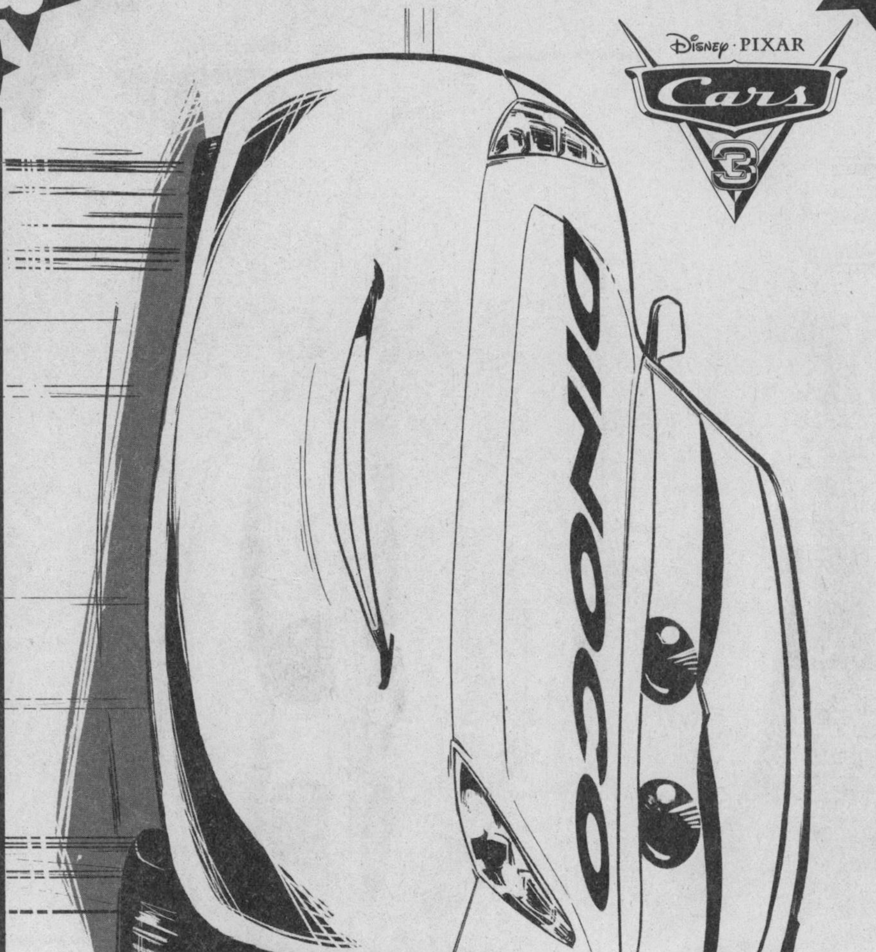

DINOCO

DINOCO 51

Cruz Ramirez is the new Dinoco Race Car.

WATCH YOUR PICTURE COME TO LIFE!

HOLD YOUR DEVICE OVER THE PICTURE UNTIL YOU SEE THE ★ IN THE CORNERS.

Disney · PIXAR Cars 3

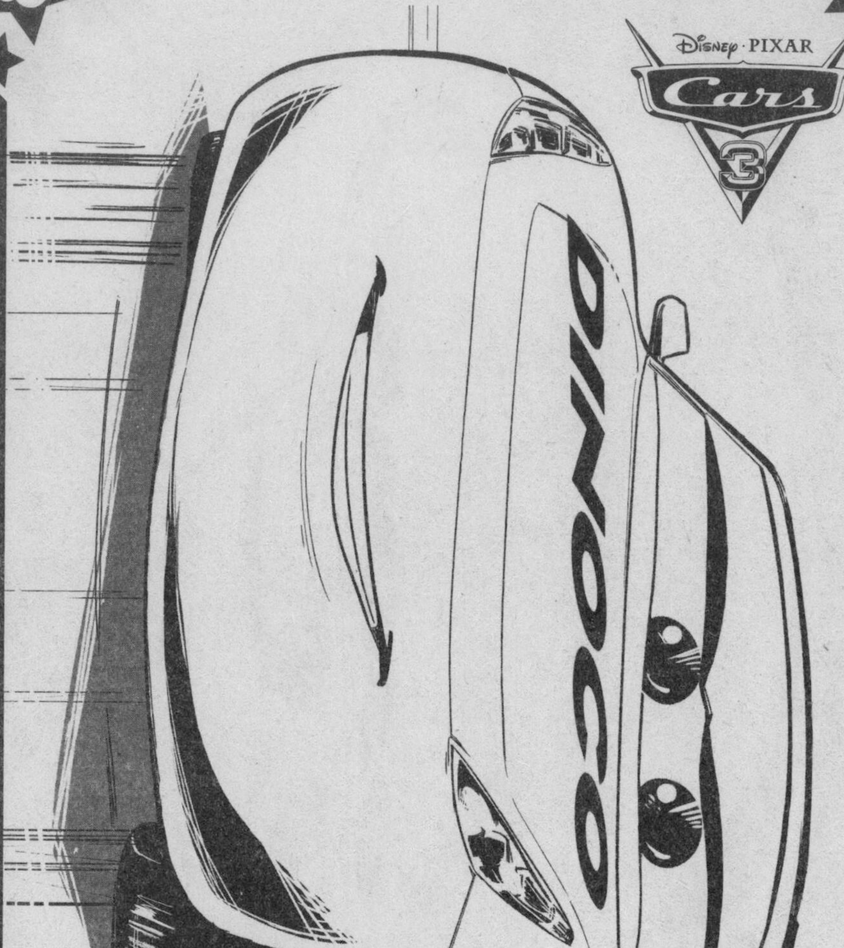

DINOCO

DINOCO 51

Cruz Ramirez is the new Dinoco Race Car.

WATCH YOUR PICTURE COME TO LIFE!

HOLD YOUR DEVICE OVER THE PICTURE UNTIL YOU SEE THE IN THE CORNERS.

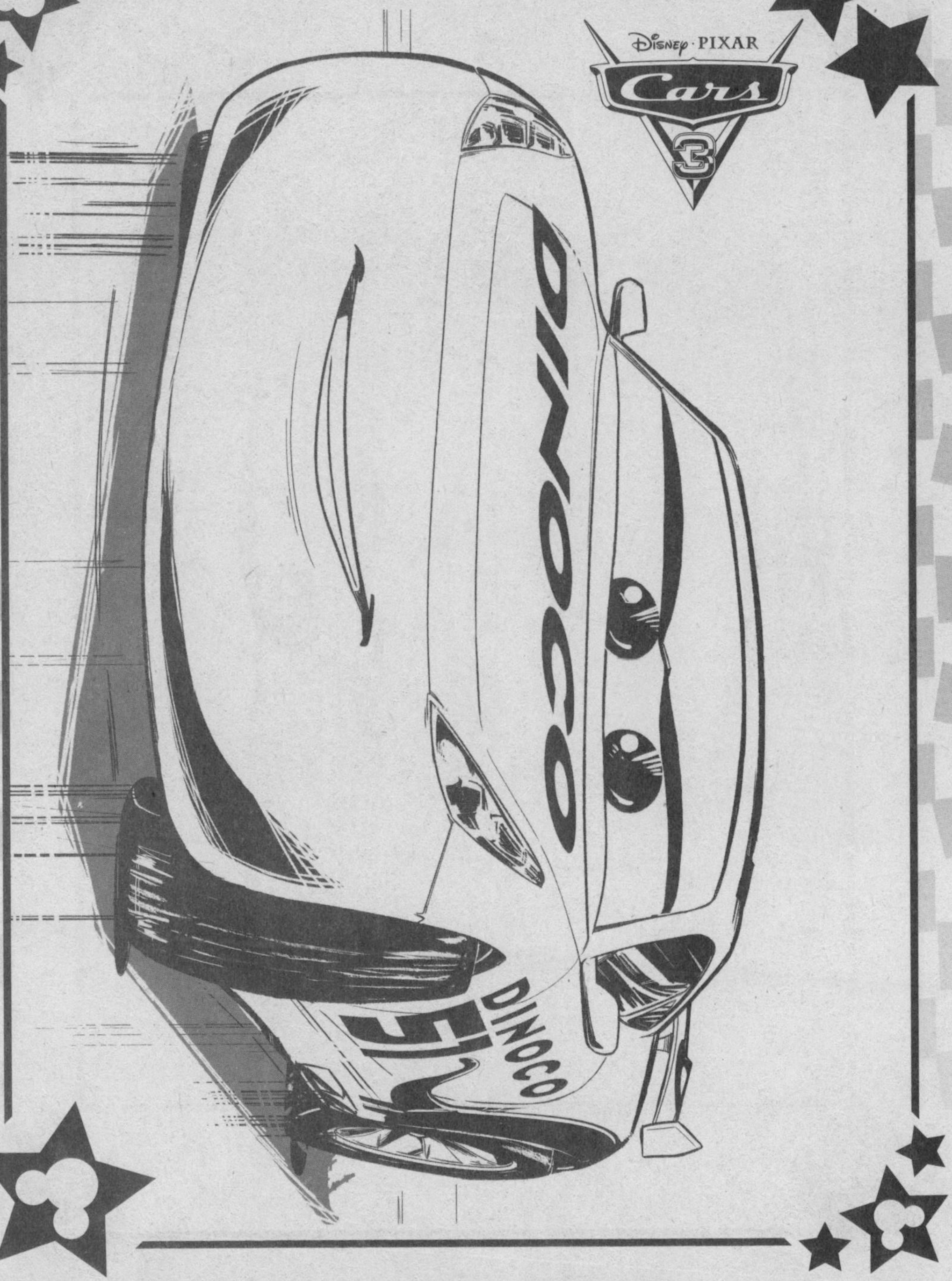

Disney · PIXAR Cars 3

DINOCO

DINOCO

51

Cruz Ramirez is the new Dinoco Race Car.

DRAW A PICTURE!

HOLD YOUR DEVICE OVER THE PICTURE UNTIL YOU SEE THE [puzzle piece] IN THE CORNERS TO MAKE A PUZZLE.

DRAW A PICTURE!

HOLD YOUR DEVICE OVER THE PICTURE UNTIL YOU SEE THE IN THE CORNERS TO MAKE A PUZZLE.

DRAW A PICTURE!

HOLD YOUR DEVICE OVER THE PICTURE UNTIL YOU SEE THE IN THE CORNERS TO MAKE A PUZZLE.

DRAW A PICTURE!

HOLD YOUR DEVICE OVER THE PICTURE UNTIL YOU SEE THE IN THE CORNERS TO MAKE A PUZZLE.

WATCH YOUR PICTURE COME TO LIFE!

HOLD YOUR DEVICE OVER THE PICTURE UNTIL YOU SEE THE ★★★ IN THE CORNERS.

Disney · PIXAR Cars 3

Cruz Ramirez can't wait to wow the crowd!

WATCH YOUR PICTURE COME TO LIFE!

HOLD YOUR DEVICE OVER THE PICTURE UNTIL YOU SEE THE ★ IN THE CORNERS.

Disney · PIXAR Cars 3

Cruz Ramirez can't wait to wow the crowd!

WATCH YOUR PICTURE COME TO LIFE!

HOLD YOUR DEVICE OVER THE PICTURE UNTIL YOU SEE THE ✩ IN THE CORNERS.

Disney · PIXAR Cars 3

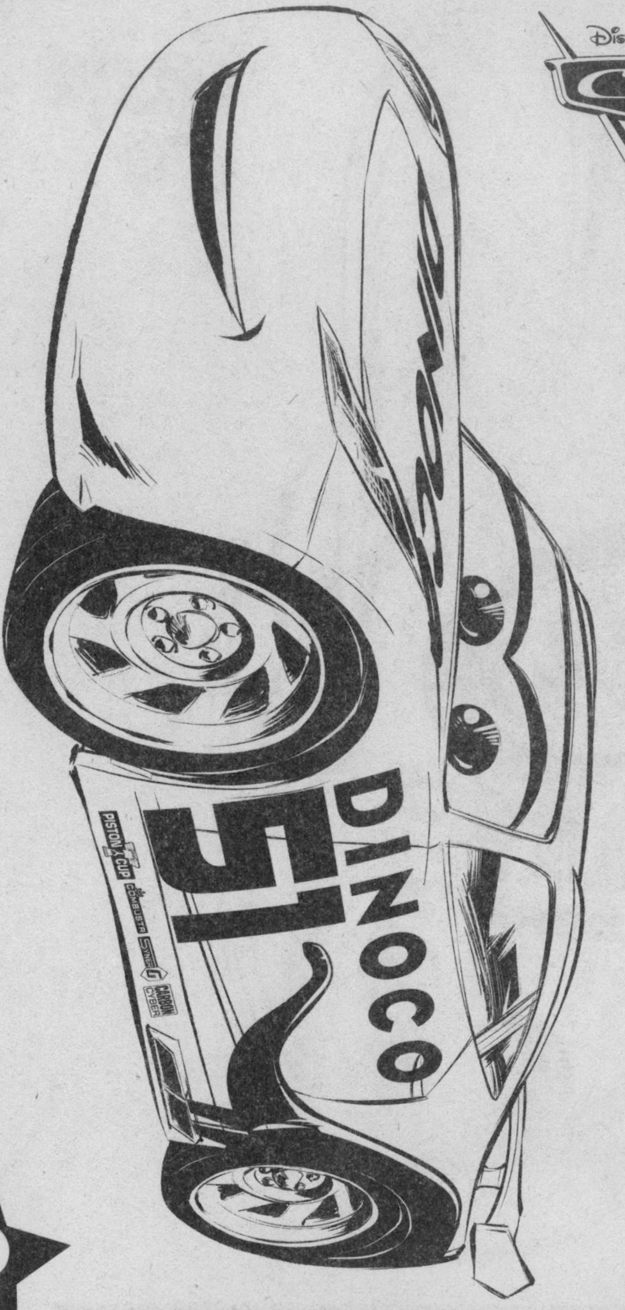

DINOCO 51

Cruz Ramirez can't wait to wow the crowd!

WATCH YOUR PICTURE COME TO LIFE!

HOLD YOUR DEVICE OVER THE PICTURE UNTIL YOU SEE THE ★ IN THE CORNERS.

Disney · PIXAR Cars 3

DINOCO 51

Cruz Ramirez can't wait to wow the crowd!

WATCH YOUR PICTURE COME TO LIFE!

HOLD YOUR DEVICE OVER THE PICTURE UNTIL YOU SEE THE ★ IN THE CORNERS.

Disney · PIXAR Cars 3

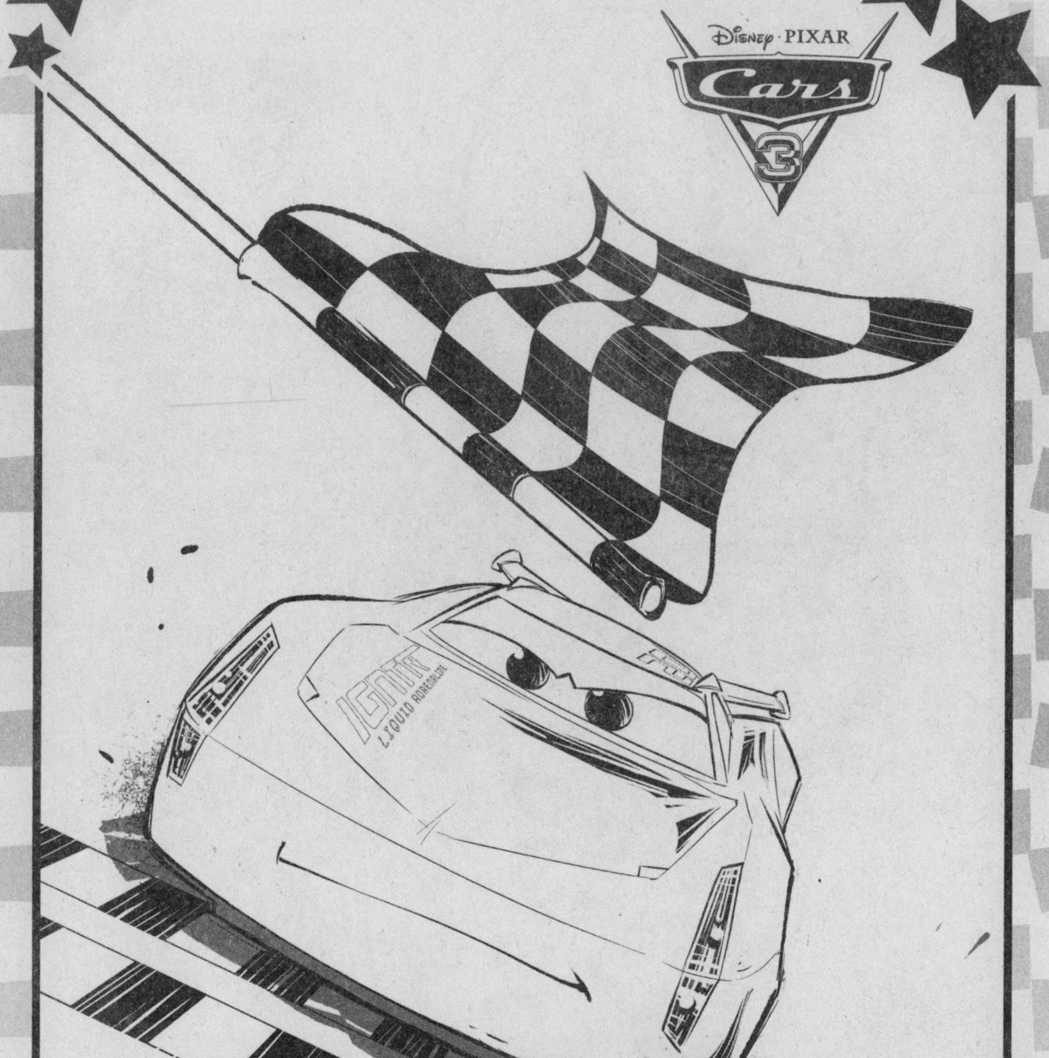

Jackson Storm crosses the finish line!

WATCH YOUR PICTURE COME TO LIFE!

HOLD YOUR DEVICE OVER THE PICTURE UNTIL YOU SEE THE ★ IN THE CORNERS.

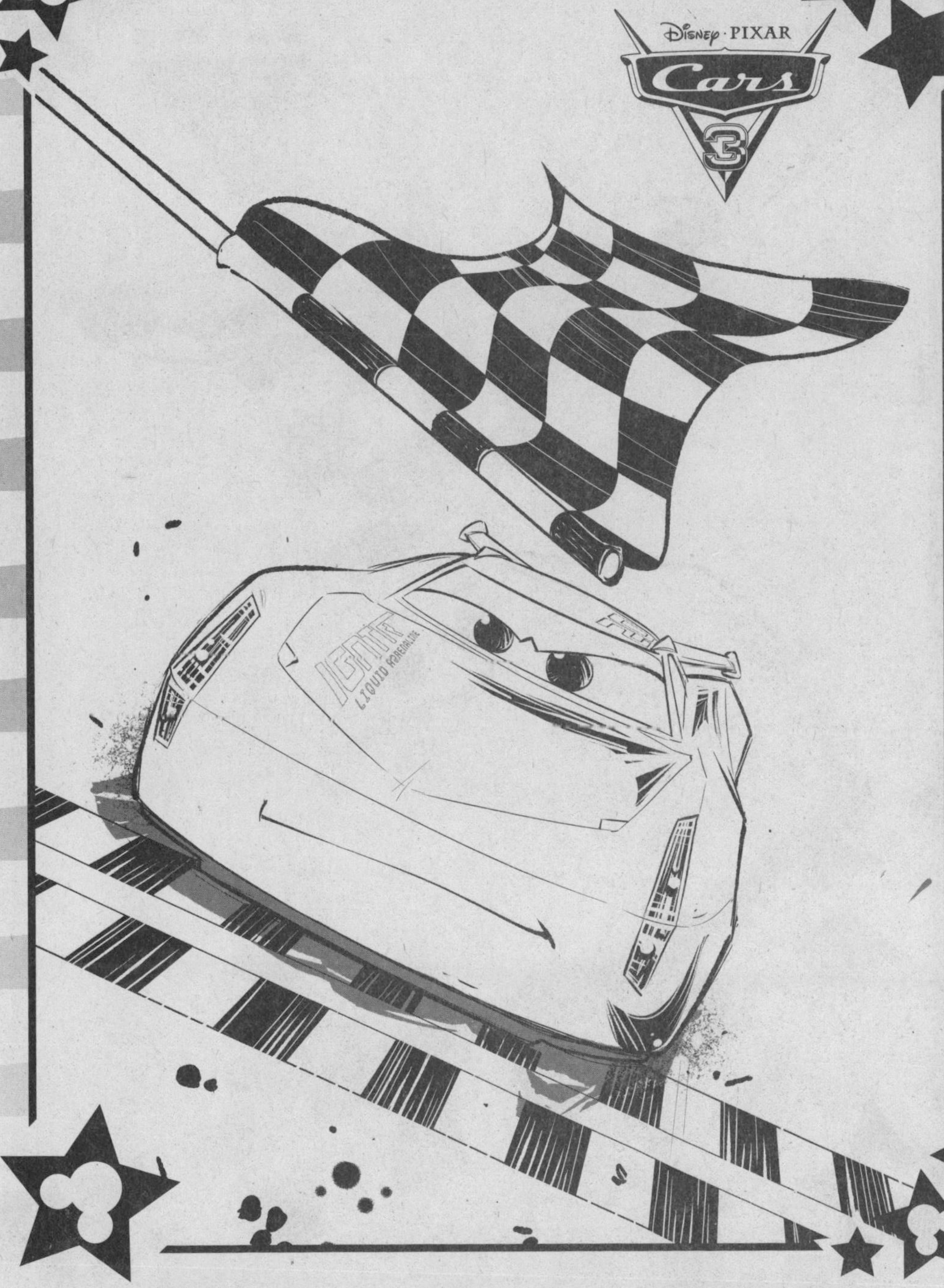

Disney · PIXAR Cars 3

Jackson Storm crosses the finish line!

WATCH YOUR PICTURE COME TO LIFE!

HOLD YOUR DEVICE OVER THE PICTURE UNTIL YOU SEE THE ★ IN THE CORNERS.

Disney · PIXAR Cars 3

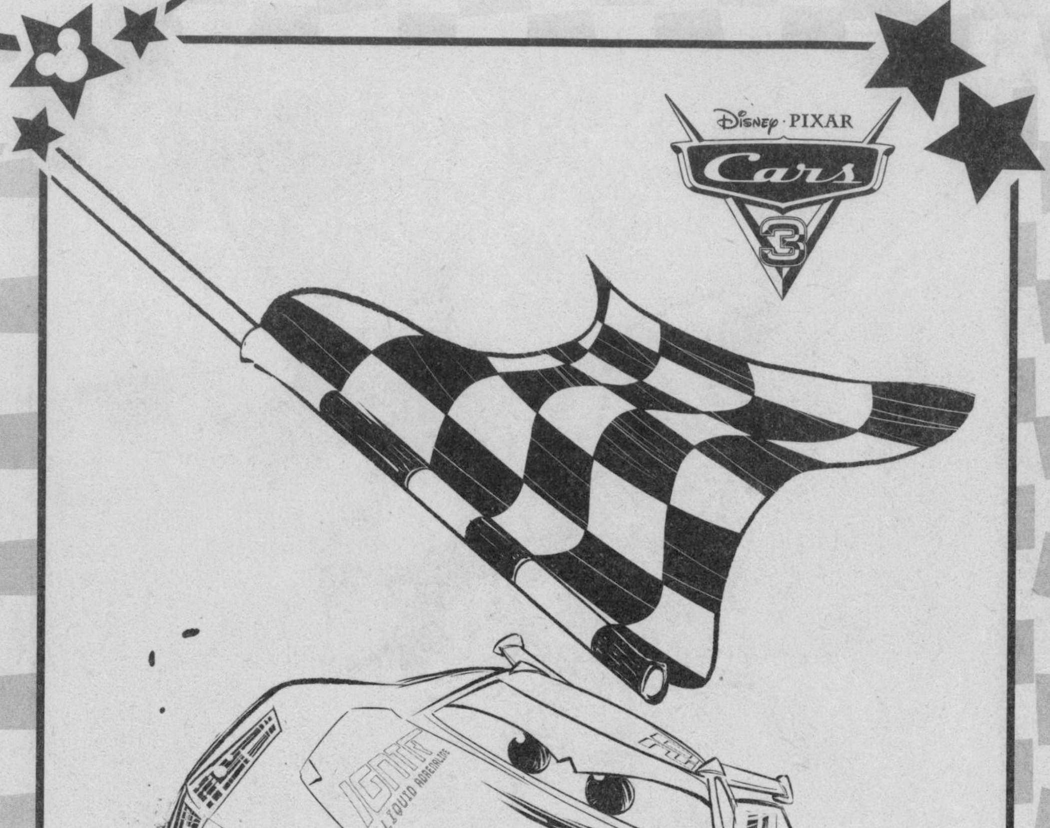

Jackson Storm crosses the finish line!

WATCH YOUR PICTURE COME TO LIFE!

HOLD YOUR DEVICE OVER THE PICTURE UNTIL YOU SEE THE ★✪★ IN THE CORNERS.

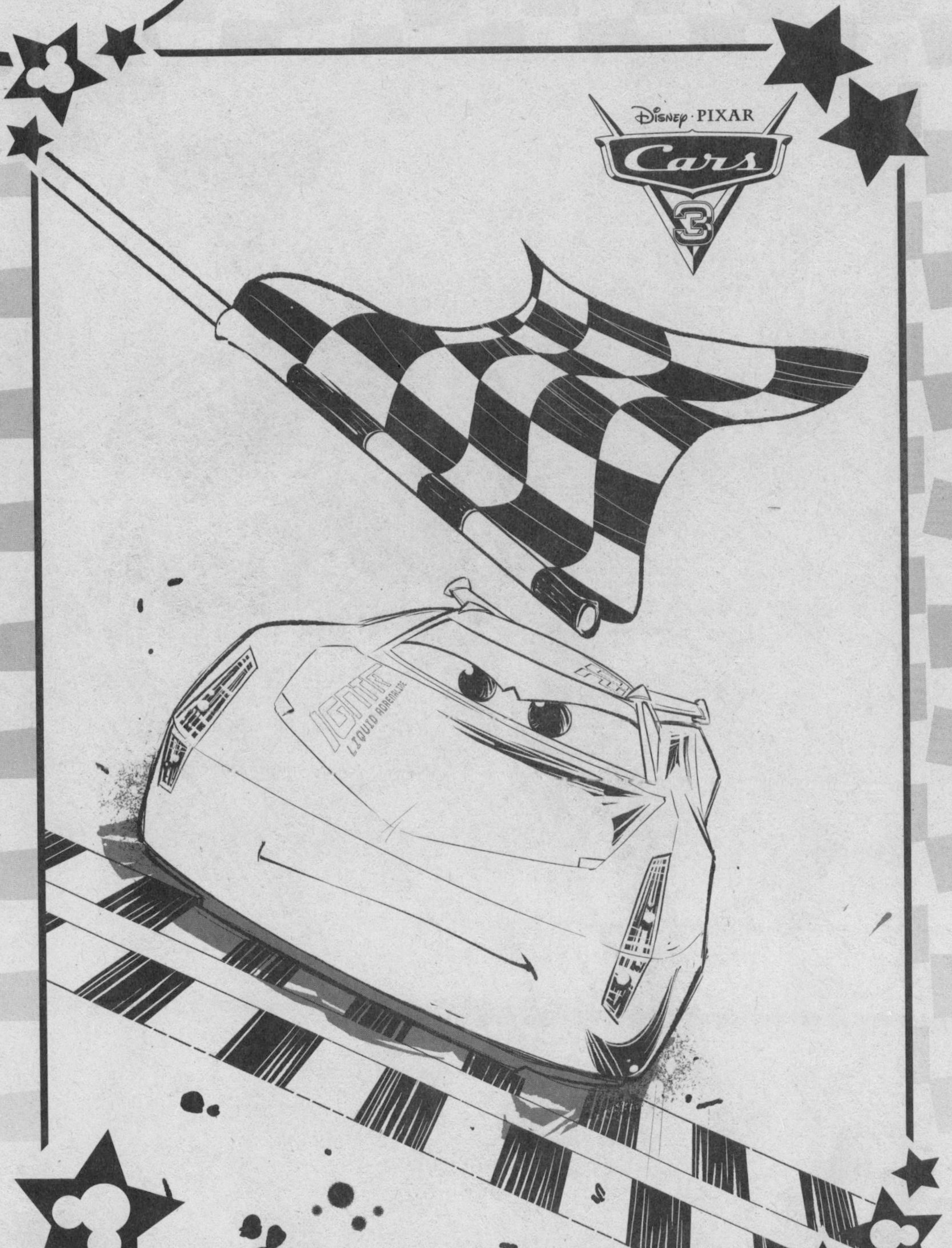

Disney · PIXAR Cars 3

Jackson Storm crosses the finish line!

WATCH YOUR PICTURE COME TO LIFE!

HOLD YOUR DEVICE OVER THE PICTURE UNTIL YOU SEE THE ★ IN THE CORNERS.

Disney · PIXAR Cars 3

Ka-chowwwww!!!

WATCH YOUR PICTURE COME TO LIFE!

HOLD YOUR DEVICE OVER THE PICTURE UNTIL YOU SEE THE ☆ IN THE CORNERS.

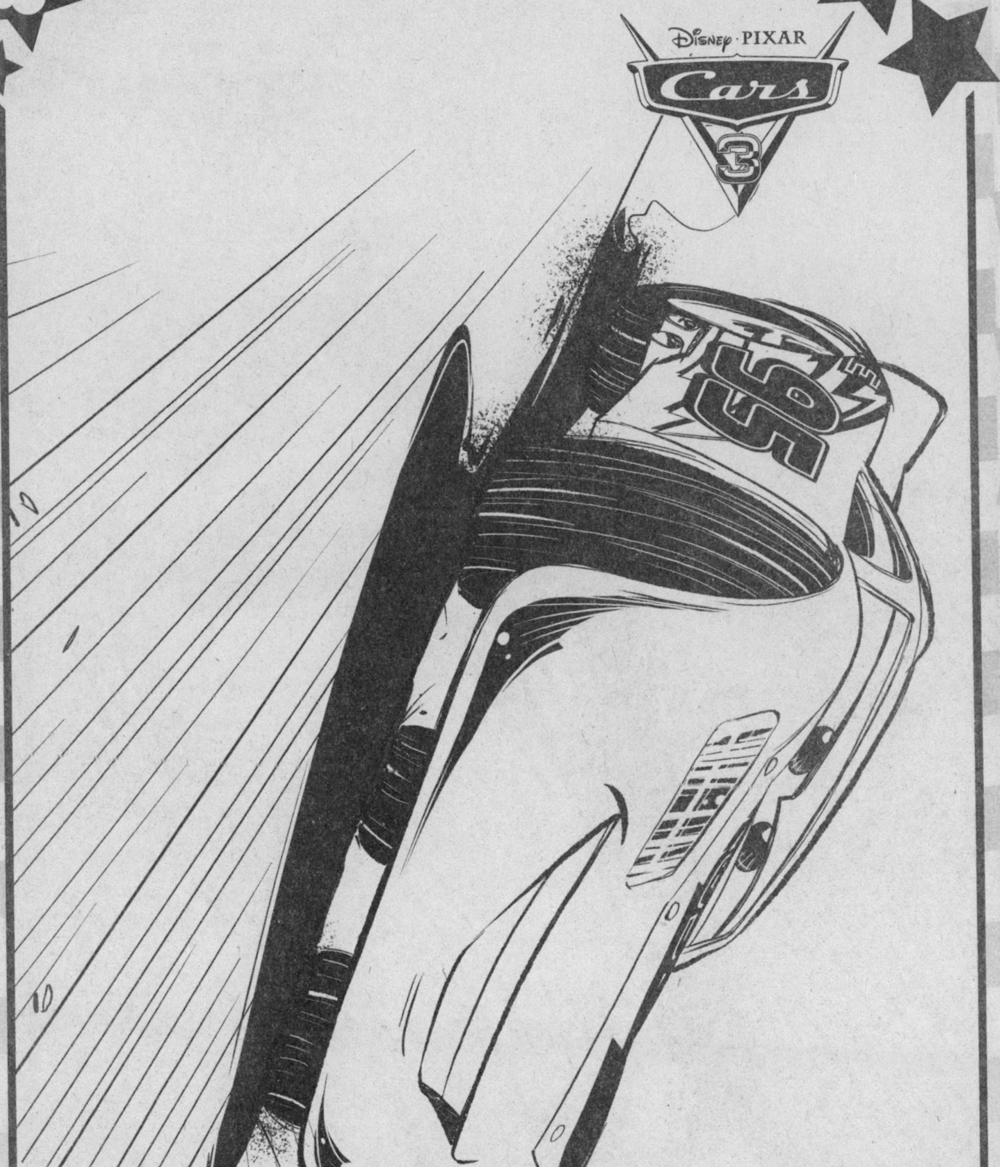

Disney · PIXAR Cars 3

Ka-chowwwwww!!!

WATCH YOUR PICTURE COME TO LIFE!

HOLD YOUR DEVICE OVER THE PICTURE UNTIL YOU SEE THE ★ IN THE CORNERS.

Disney · PIXAR Cars 3

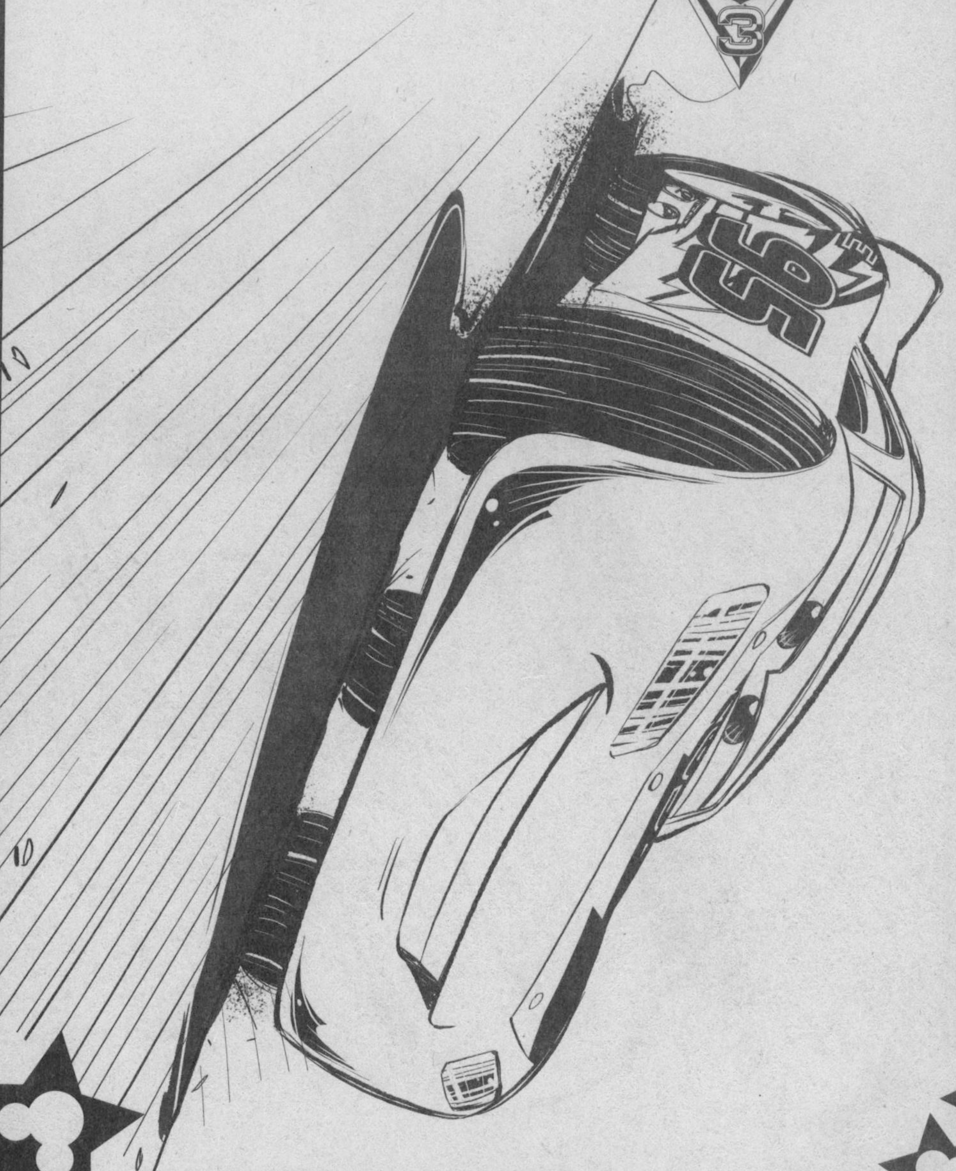

Ka-chowwwww!!!

WATCH YOUR PICTURE COME TO LIFE!

HOLD YOUR DEVICE OVER THE PICTURE UNTIL YOU SEE THE ★ IN THE CORNERS.

Disney · PIXAR Cars 3

Ka-chowwwwww!!!

WATCH YOUR PICTURE COME TO LIFE!

HOLD YOUR DEVICE OVER THE PICTURE UNTIL YOU SEE THE ★✪★ IN THE CORNERS.

Disney·PIXAR Cars 3

Jackson Storm will give Lightning McQueen a run for his money.

WATCH YOUR PICTURE COME TO LIFE!

HOLD YOUR DEVICE OVER THE PICTURE UNTIL YOU SEE THE ★ IN THE CORNERS.

Disney · PIXAR
Cars 3

Jackson Storm will give Lightning McQueen a run for his money.

WATCH YOUR PICTURE COME TO LIFE!

HOLD YOUR DEVICE OVER THE PICTURE UNTIL YOU SEE THE ★ IN THE CORNERS.

Disney · PIXAR Cars 3

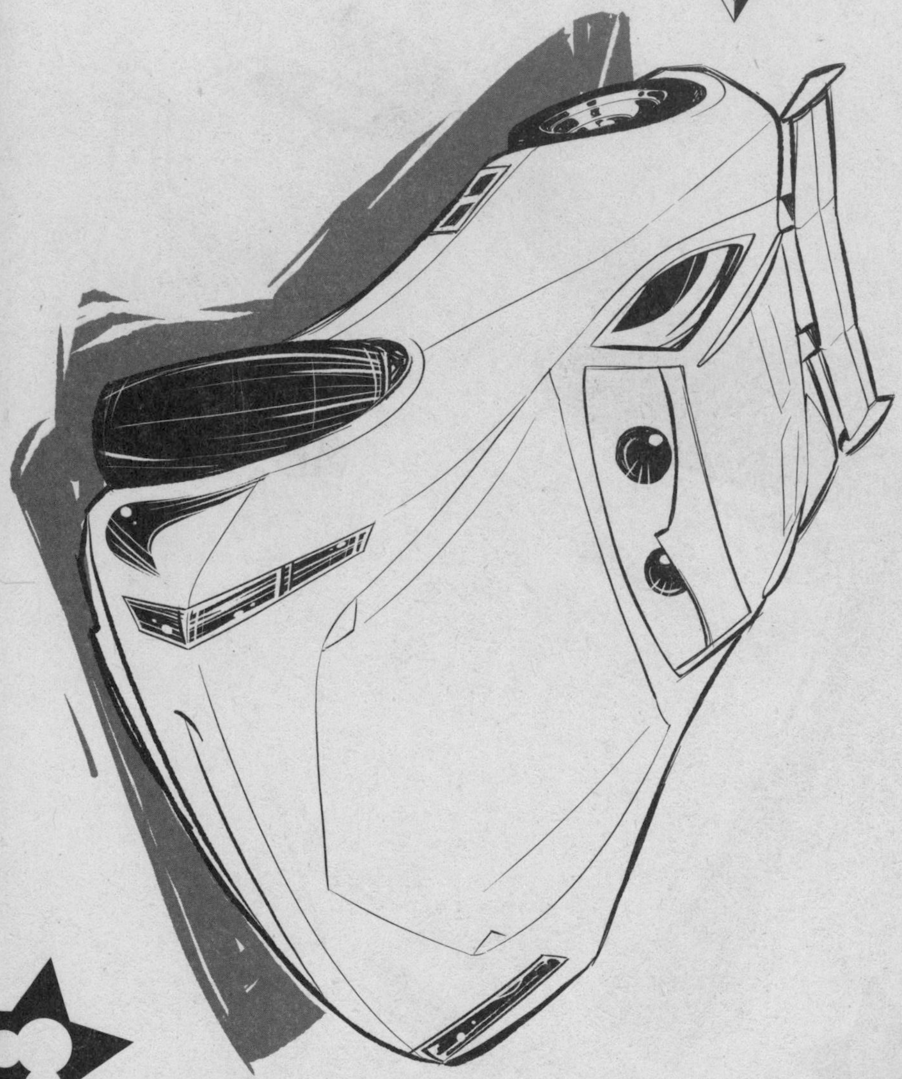

Jackson Storm will give Lightning McQueen a run for his money.

WATCH YOUR PICTURE COME TO LIFE!

HOLD YOUR DEVICE OVER THE PICTURE UNTIL YOU SEE THE ★ IN THE CORNERS.

Disney · PIXAR Cars 3

Jackson Storm will give Lightning McQueen a run for his money.

WATCH YOUR PICTURE COME TO LIFE!

HOLD YOUR DEVICE OVER THE PICTURE UNTIL YOU SEE THE ★ IN THE CORNERS.

Disney · PIXAR Cars 3

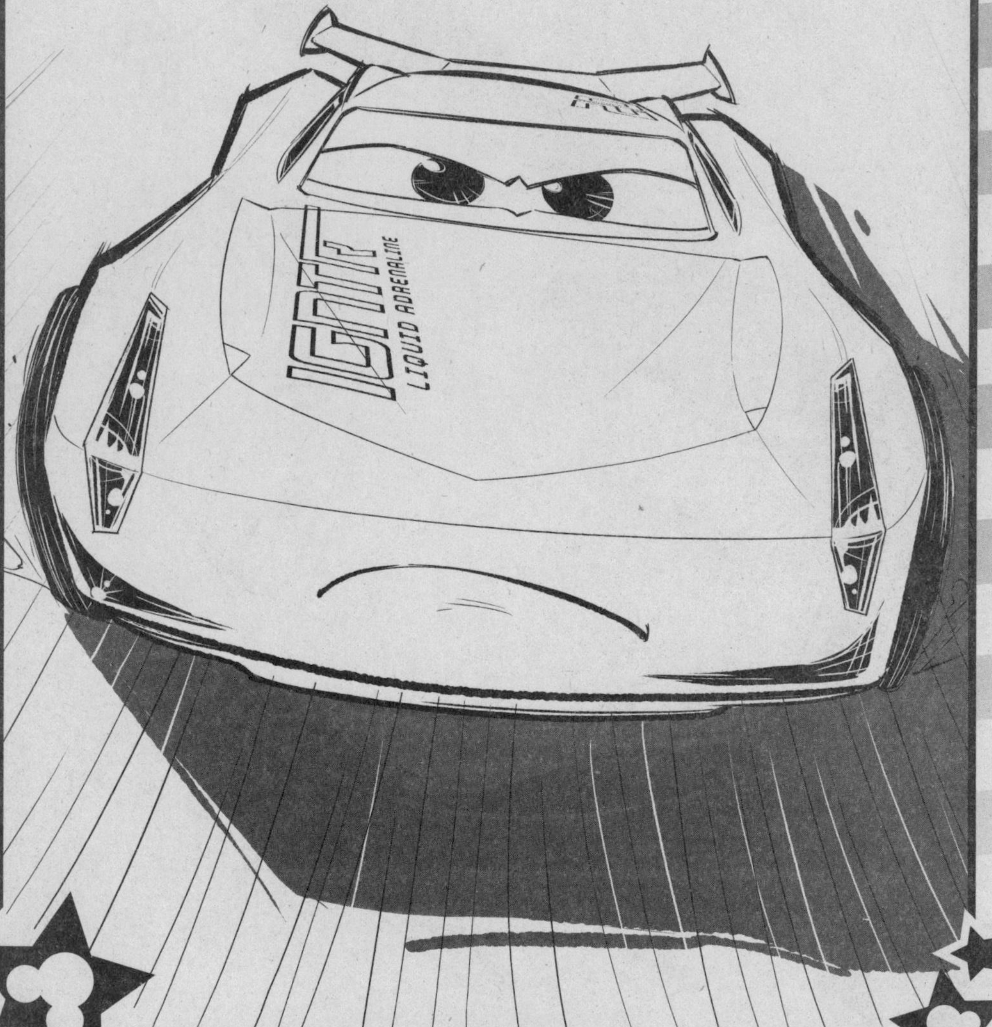

IGNTR LIQUID ADRENALINE

Jackson Storm puts on his game face.

WATCH YOUR PICTURE COME TO LIFE!

HOLD YOUR DEVICE OVER THE PICTURE UNTIL YOU SEE THE IN THE CORNERS.

Disney · PIXAR Cars 3

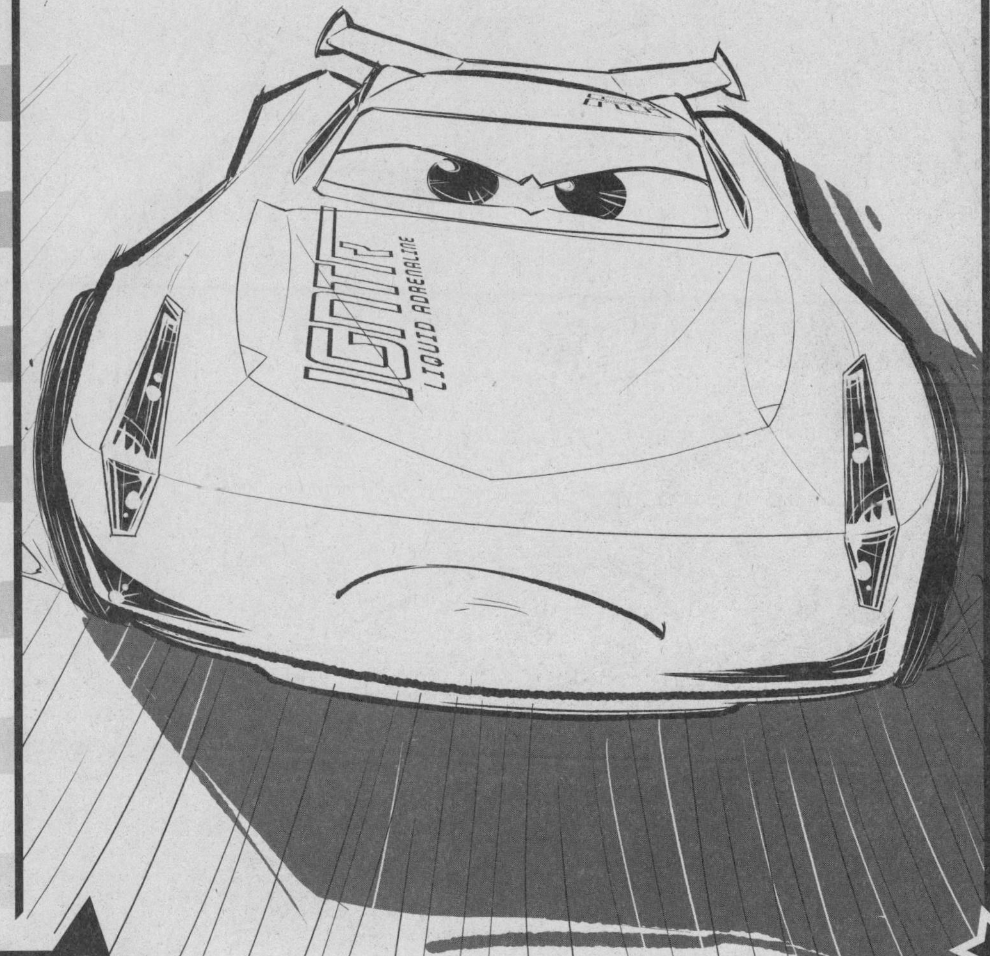

Jackson Storm puts on his game face.

WATCH YOUR PICTURE COME TO LIFE!

HOLD YOUR DEVICE OVER THE PICTURE UNTIL YOU SEE THE ★ IN THE CORNERS.

Disney · PIXAR Cars 3

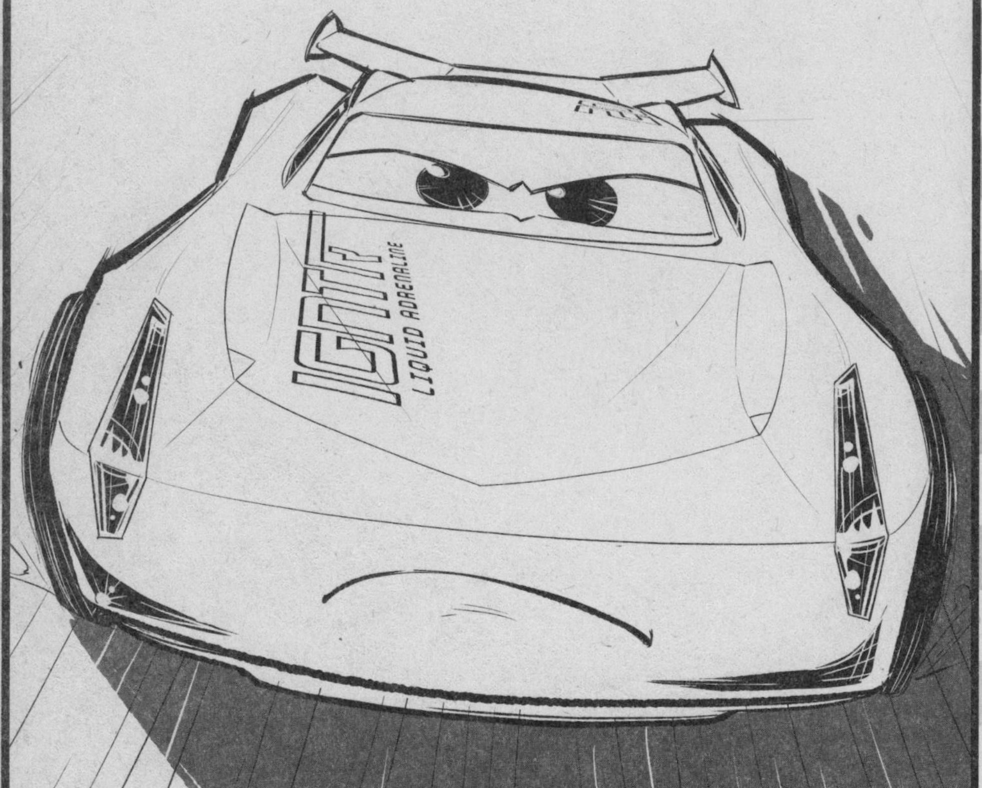

IGNTR LIQUID ADRENALINE

Jackson Storm puts on his game face.

WATCH YOUR PICTURE COME TO LIFE!

HOLD YOUR DEVICE OVER THE PICTURE UNTIL YOU SEE THE ★ IN THE CORNERS.

Disney · PIXAR Cars 3

IGNTR LIQUID ADRENALINE

Jackson Storm puts on his game face.

WATCH YOUR PICTURE COME TO LIFE!

HOLD YOUR DEVICE OVER THE PICTURE UNTIL YOU SEE THE ★ IN THE CORNERS.

Disney·Pixar Cars 3

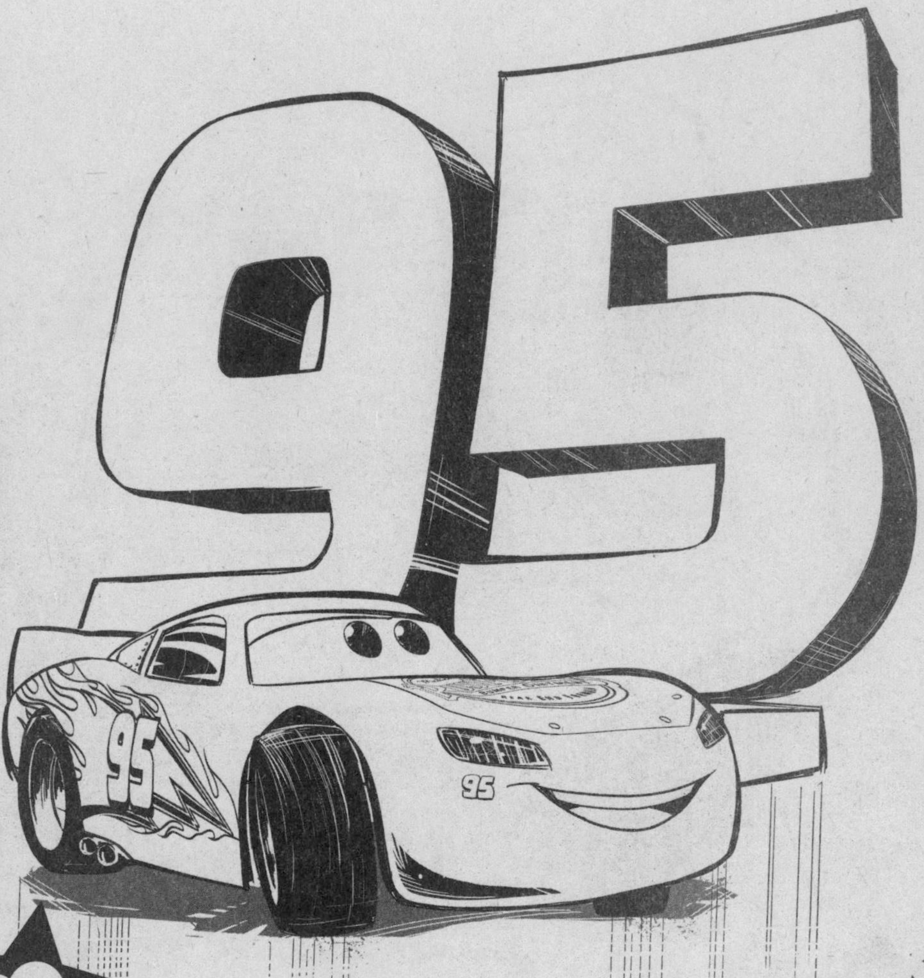

95

95 is a very important number to Lightning McQueen.

WATCH YOUR PICTURE COME TO LIFE!

HOLD YOUR DEVICE OVER THE PICTURE UNTIL YOU SEE THE ✩ IN THE CORNERS.

Disney · PIXAR Cars 3

95 is a very important number to Lightning McQueen.

WATCH YOUR PICTURE COME TO LIFE!

HOLD YOUR DEVICE OVER THE PICTURE UNTIL YOU SEE THE ★ IN THE CORNERS.

Disney · PIXAR Cars 3

95

95 is a very important number to Lightning McQueen.

WATCH YOUR PICTURE COME TO LIFE!

HOLD YOUR DEVICE OVER THE PICTURE UNTIL YOU SEE THE ★ IN THE CORNERS.

Disney · PIXAR
Cars 3

95 is a very important number to Lightning McQueen.

Lightning McQueen is a famous race car.

Lightning speeds past the other racers.

LIGHTNING MCQUEEN

RADIATOR
SPONSORS
CHAMPION
SPRINGS
CRASH
KACHOW
FAMOUS
CAREER
VETERAN
PISTON CUP
TRAINER
LEGEND
TRACK
RUST-EZE
FANS
BRAND

LIGHTNING MCQUEEN

S	P	R	I	N	G	S	R	E	K	B	N	I
N	S	R	O	T	A	I	D	A	R	V	N	F
A	R	P	X	N	V	D	L	I	T	D	E	U
F	O	C	I	F	K	C	A	R	T	Z	L	N
X	S	P	Y	S	Y	O	E	S	E	E	O	Y
Z	N	F	W	S	T	N	P	T	G	I	D	Q
B	O	Q	R	C	I	O	S	E	P	R	M	N
R	P	U	J	A	F	U	N	M	Q	W	W	D
A	S	D	R	R	R	D	A	C	O	U	J	X
N	F	T	K	E	G	H	R	H	U	N	K	V
D	N	K	A	E	C	A	C	J	U	P	C	F
N	B	M	J	R	S	A	S	G	X	P	O	L
K	I	D	I	H	K	F	A	M	O	U	S	B
V	E	T	E	R	A	N	Q	P	B	X	C	S

46'S > 33 DEGREE BANK > .40 DR

Which picture of Lightning is different?
A
B
C
D
Your Answer:
4G'S > 33 DEGREE BANK > .40 DR

Answer: C

Long ago, Doc Hudson was Lightning's coach and crew chief.

Guido and Luigi are always ready to help
Lightning during his pit stop.

Lightning McQueen's two biggest fans: Mater and Sally!

nswer: 23

Tex is the owner of Dinoco. He wants Lightning McQueen to race for his team.

CARS

LIGHTNING
GUIDO
JACKSON STORM
MACK
MCQUEEN
LUIGI
CHICK HICKS
DOC HUDSON
MATER
NATALIE CERTAIN
CAL WEATHERS
SALLY
RUSTY
BOBBY SWIFT
TEX
DUSTY

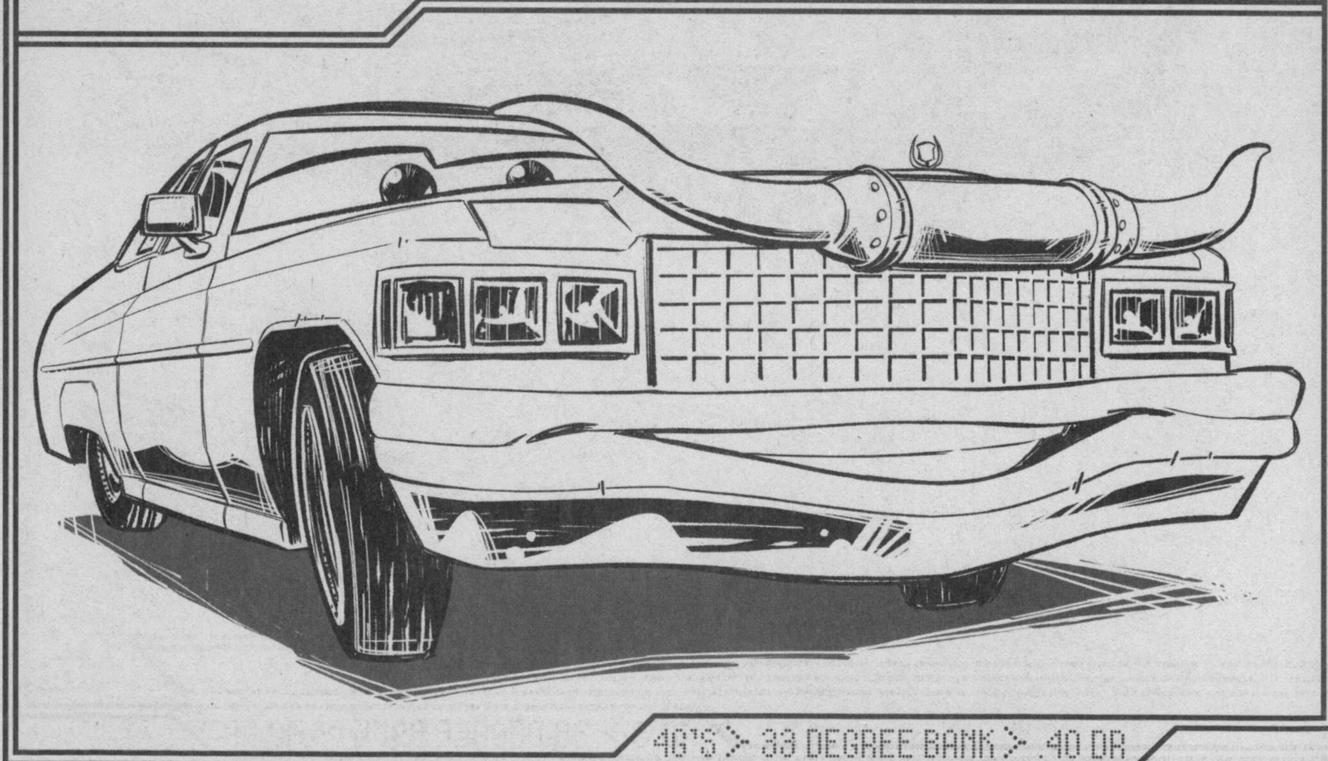

CARS

T	R	N	O	S	D	U	H	C	O	D	I	B
B	U	I	Y	T	S	U	D	W	U	G	O	R
X	S	A	E	N	G	K	M	U	I	B	M	N
B	T	T	S	G	U	C	X	U	B	U	R	E
D	Y	R	Q	I	I	A	L	Y	S	K	O	E
U	H	E	L	A	G	L	S	Y	K	C	T	U
M	T	C	I	C	X	W	J	R	C	A	S	Q
A	P	E	G	B	I	E	R	M	I	M	N	C
T	S	I	H	F	G	A	O	Q	H	M	O	M
E	A	L	T	R	P	T	D	U	K	J	S	H
R	L	A	N	T	A	H	I	X	C	U	K	L
F	L	T	I	E	J	E	U	H	I	M	C	O
X	Y	A	N	X	I	R	G	Q	H	V	A	J
X	W	N	G	Y	B	S	M	W	C	B	J	T

40'S > 33 DEGREE BANK > .40 DR

HICKS

Chick Hicks was Lightning's racing rival.
Now Chick hosts his own television show.

DOT-TO-DOT

Match each character on the right with the shadow on the left.

swer: A-3, B-1, C-2

Natalie Certain knows her numbers!
She is an expert at predicting winners.

MORE CARS

STERLING
SMOKEY
DANNY SWERVEZ
TACO
CRUZ RAMIREZ
RIVER SCOTT
BRICK YARDLEY
CHASE RACELOTT
MISS FRITTER
LOUISE NASH
ARVY
CHIP GEARINGS
MR. DRIPPY
JUNIOR MOON
DOCTOR DAMAGE
RAMONE

40'S > 33 DEGREE BANK > .40 DR

MORE CARS

S	C	C	R	U	Z	R	A	M	I	R	E	Z
C	H	I	P	G	E	A	R	I	N	G	S	L
S	A	L	O	U	O	L	B	I	A	D	B	O
T	S	R	G	C	J	Y	Y	M	R	A	R	U
E	E	D	A	I	V	E	A	I	N	N	I	I
R	R	T	G	R	K	D	V	S	O	N	C	S
L	A	B	A	O	R	E	Y	S	O	Y	K	E
I	C	L	M	O	R	U	P	F	M	S	Y	N
N	E	S	T	S	P	E	P	R	R	W	A	A
G	L	C	C	U	Q	N	I	I	O	E	R	S
Q	O	O	K	P	Q	O	R	T	I	R	D	H
D	T	K	R	Q	D	M	D	T	N	V	L	Q
T	T	R	S	M	U	A	R	E	U	E	E	G
N	A	D	V	G	F	R	M	R	J	Z	Y	P

Rusty and Dusty are Lightning McQueen's sponsors.

Mack is ready for the long haul.

The Radiator Springs gang gathers onMain Street to say good-bye to Lightning.

Use the grid to draw Guido.

4G'S > 33 DEGREE BANK > .40 DR

How many words can you make with the letters in:

LIGHTNING MCQUEEN

___________________ ___________________

___________________ ___________________

___________________ ___________________

___________________ ___________________

___________________ ___________________

___________________ ___________________

___________________ ___________________

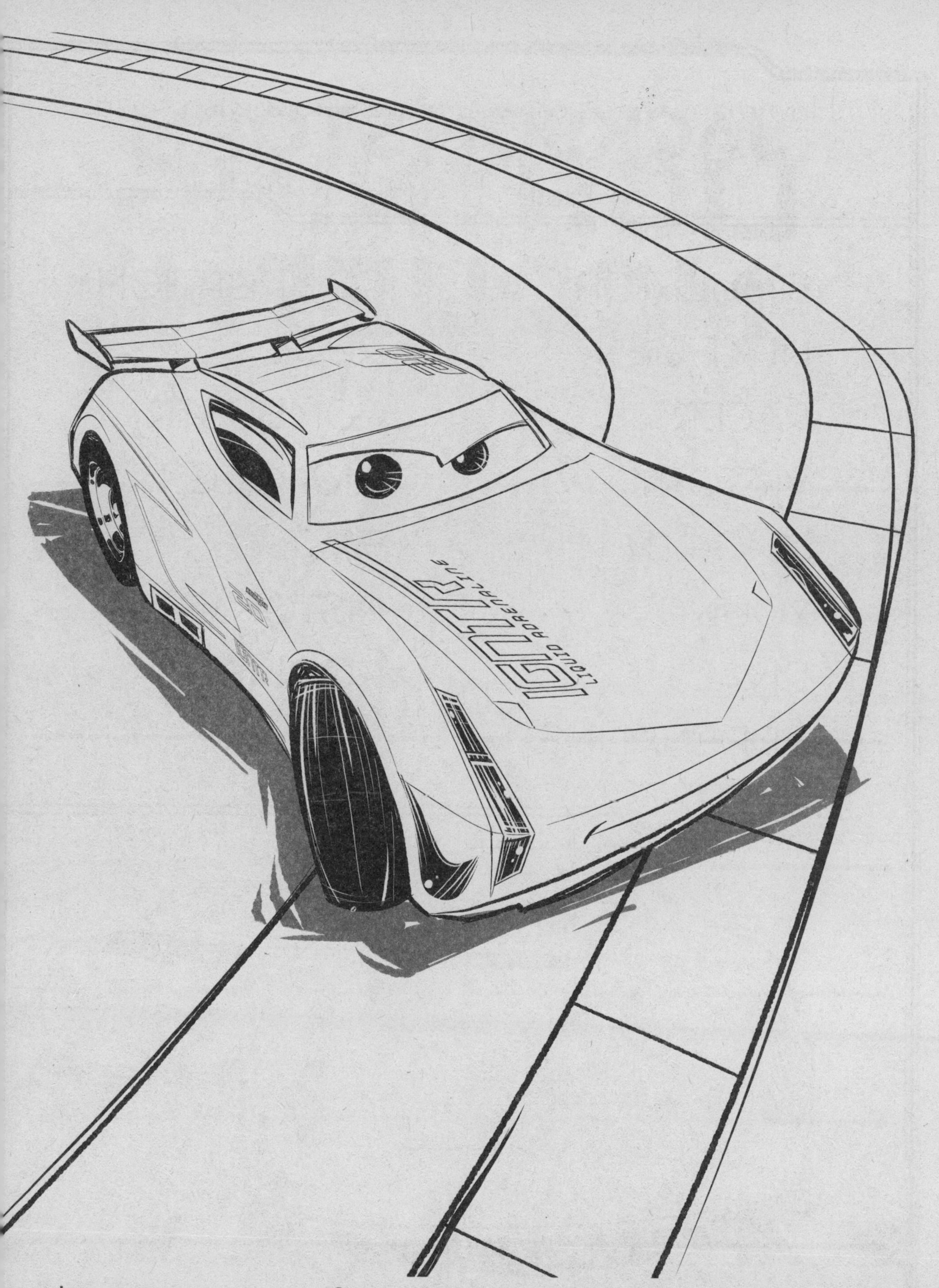

Jackson Storm is one fast racer. He only cares about winning.

JACKSON STORM

SIMULATOR
NEXT-GEN
RACER
VICTORY
JS IGNTR
YOUNG
RIVAL
ADRENALINE
COMPETITION
RUDE
COMBUSTR
HIGH TECH
FAST
PISTON CUP
ROOKIE
WINNING

JACKSON STORM

C	Y	C	Z	H	A	L	V	O	T	P	J	W
S	S	F	O	A	F	T	R	R	U	D	E	V
O	A	I	R	M	N	E	X	T	G	E	N	T
S	R	A	M	T	P	X	D	Z	F	A	S	T
G	T	E	V	U	S	E	C	R	E	C	A	R
N	N	N	T	K	L	U	T	J	U	Z	I	P
U	G	I	L	I	H	A	B	I	D	I	R	I
O	I	L	R	W	I	W	T	M	T	O	Y	S
Y	S	A	I	I	G	J	K	O	O	I	R	T
S	J	N	V	N	H	L	M	K	R	C	O	O
X	W	E	A	N	T	N	I	Y	N	R	T	N
F	D	R	L	I	E	E	J	T	F	Q	C	C
X	W	D	C	N	C	C	D	M	Z	Q	I	U
X	L	A	P	G	H	O	T	Q	Z	M	V	P

46'S > 33 DEGREE BANK > .40 DR

Which line leads Lightning to Jackson Storm?

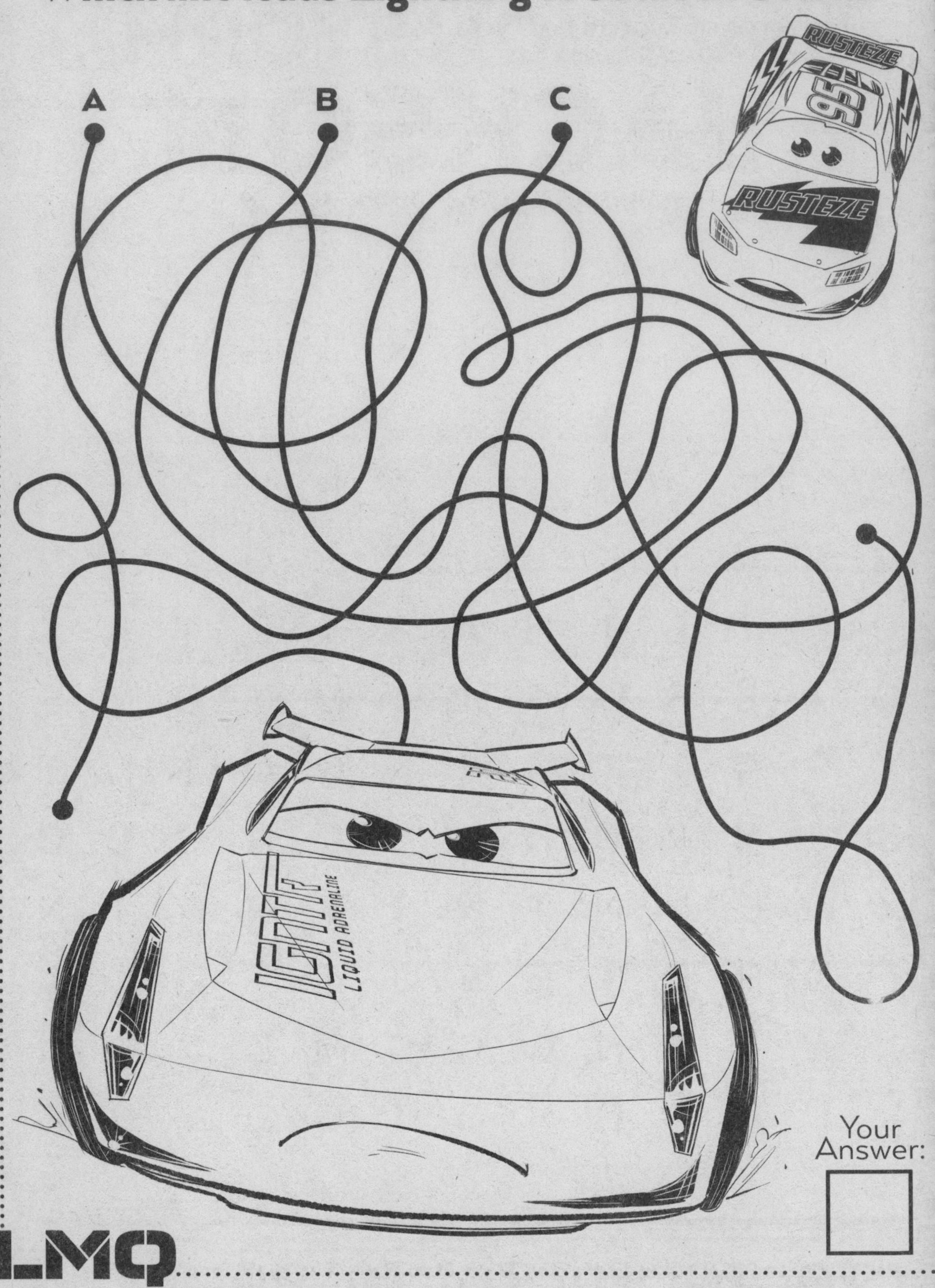

swer: B

How many words can you make with the letters in:

JACKSON STORM

Sterling is Lightning's new sponsor.

Which picture of Jackson is different?

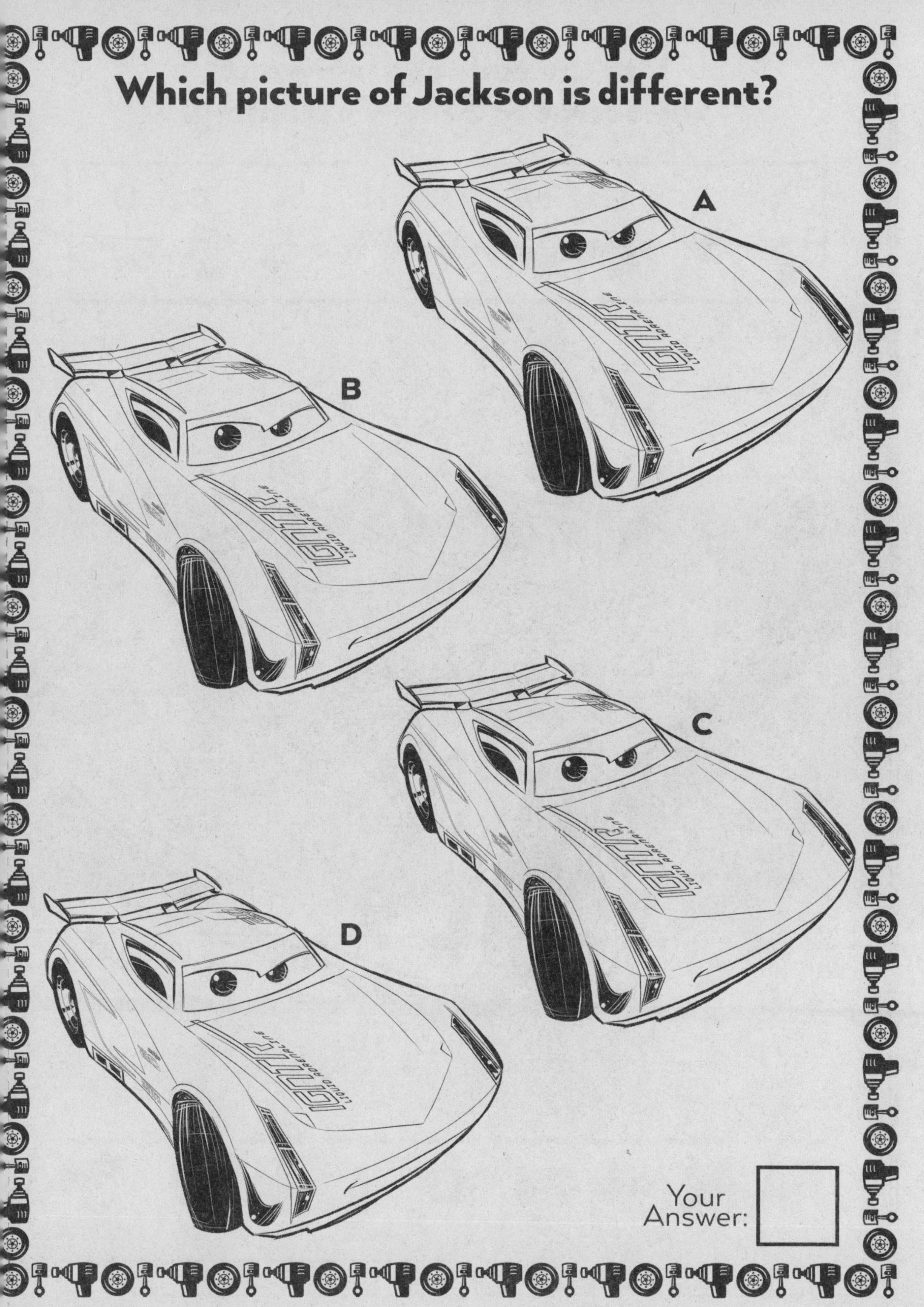

Use the code to figure out the secret to Storm's training.

A I L M O R S T U

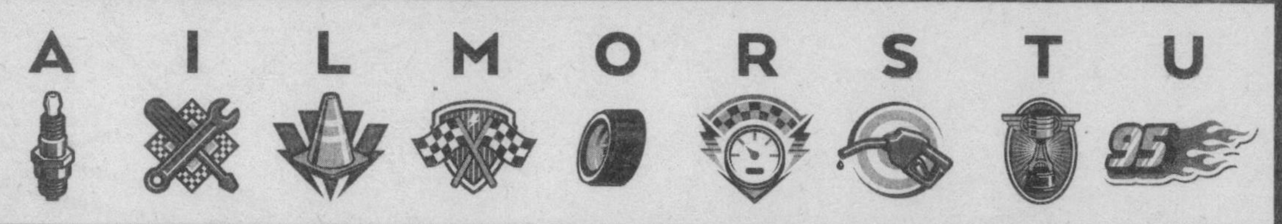

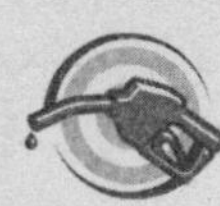

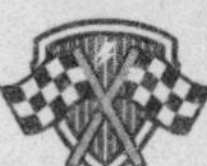

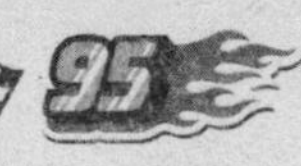

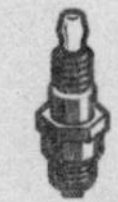

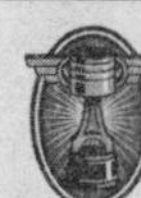

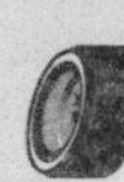

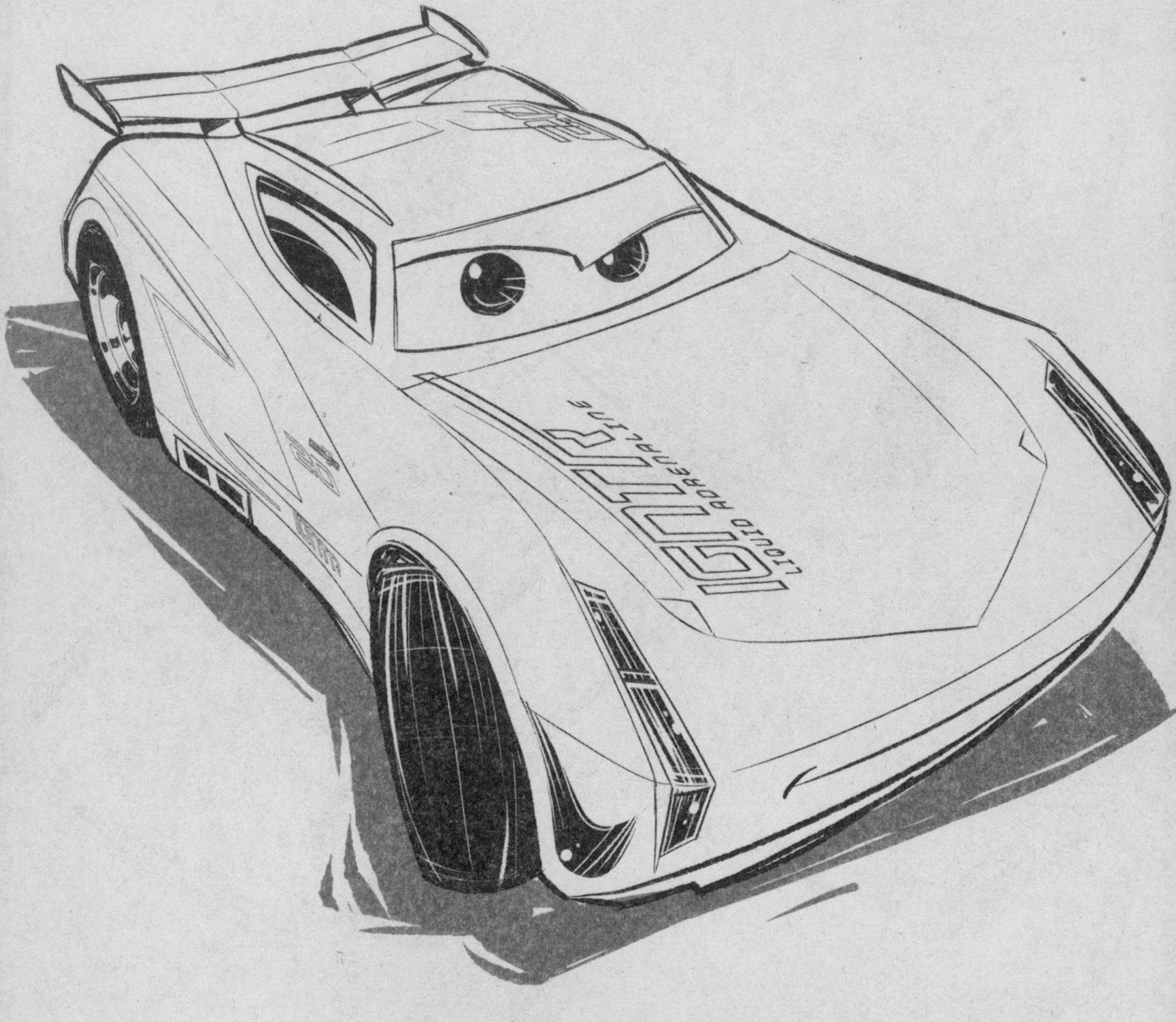

__ __ __ __ __ __ __ __ __

4G'S > 33 DEGREE BANK > .40 DR

swer: Simulator

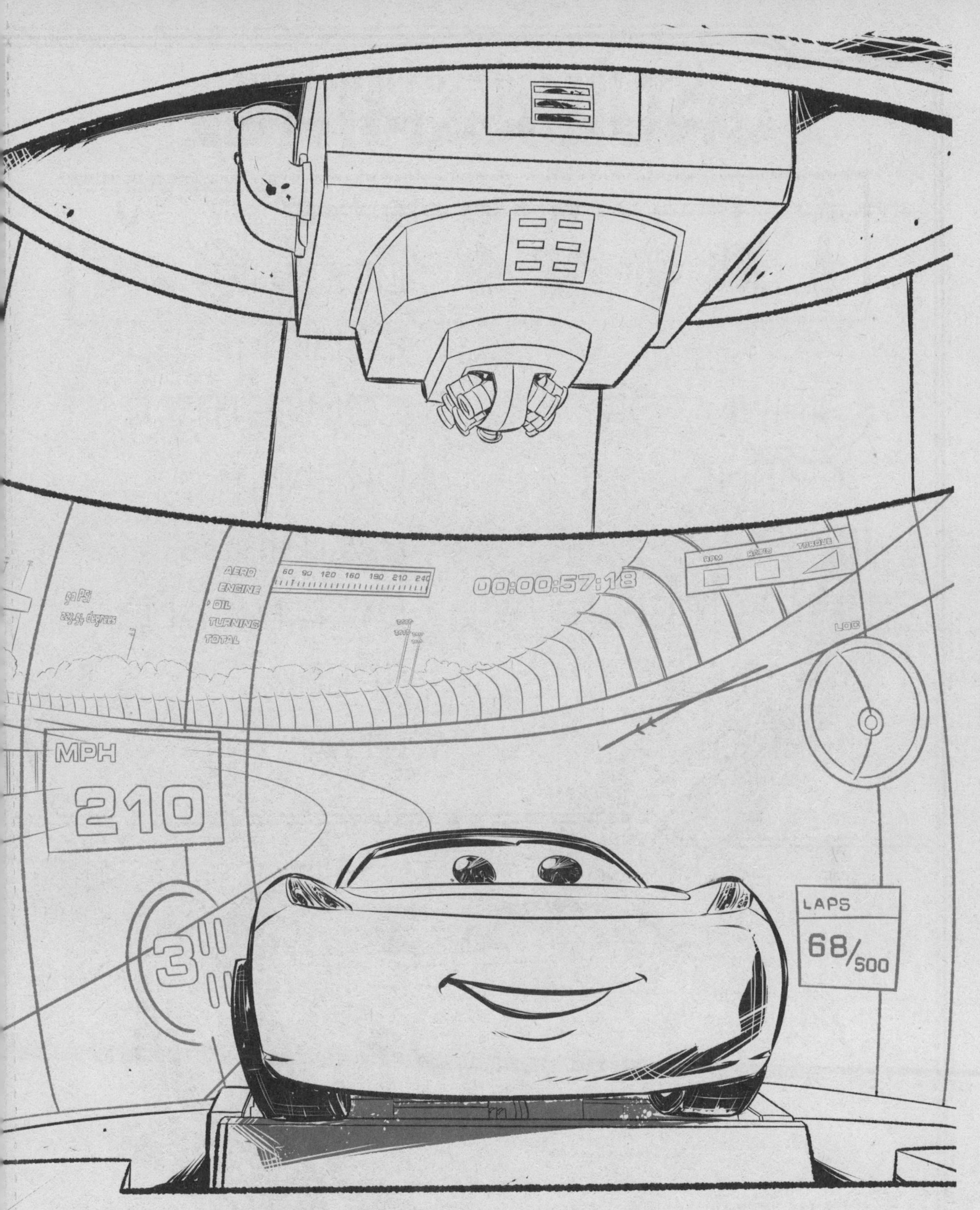

Cruz Ramirez speeds on the simulator.

CRUZ RAMIREZ

YOUNG
FAST
SIMULATOR
FRIEND
RACER
HIGH TECH
TRAINER
FIERCE
DESTINED
EQUIPMENT
COMPETITOR
DREAMS
MACHINES
DYNAMICALLY
SPEED
NEW

4G'S > 33 DEGREE BANK > .40 DR

CRUZ RAMIREZ

S	G	B	A	S	P	E	E	D	J	L	V	Q
N	E	Q	U	I	P	M	E	N	T	D	C	B
U	P	M	A	C	H	I	N	E	S	U	A	E
F	I	E	R	C	E	I	Q	P	A	D	R	V
R	H	C	E	T	H	G	I	H	Y	F	E	K
N	O	D	D	S	A	B	Q	N	Q	K	N	X
T	G	T	E	R	O	T	A	L	U	M	I	S
O	R	W	I	N	F	M	S	Y	Q	F	A	V
Q	B	E	C	T	I	V	O	M	A	R	R	Y
H	H	N	C	C	E	T	R	T	A	I	T	X
L	Q	E	A	A	J	P	S	M	J	E	H	L
I	I	L	V	Z	R	A	M	E	V	N	R	H
C	L	Y	R	C	F	K	L	O	D	D	R	D
Y	D	G	N	U	O	Y	B	Z	C	G	E	V

40'S > 33 DEGREE BANK > .40 DR

Cruz will be Lightning's new trainer.

Use the grid to draw Cruz Ramirez.

LMQ

SQUARES WITH LIGHTNING AND CRUZ

Player #1 (Lightning) draws a line to connect two dots. (You can draw up and down, or across, but not diagonally). Then Player #2 (Cruz) connects two dots. At some point, a player will connect two dots that will complete a square. Yay! That player puts a L (if the player is Lightning) or a C (if the player is Cruz) inside the square, and then gets to take another turn. When all the dots are connected, the game is over. Squares with a flag are worth one bonus point each. The competitor with the highest score is the winner.

Lightning's Score: ______ **Cruz's Score:** ______

Lightning and Cruz meet some of the other racers.

Look out! It's Miss Fritter!

The race is a demolition derby!
Lightning does not want to get crushed.

DEMOLITION DERBY

THUNDER HOLLOW
DISGUISE
MISS FRITTER
CRUSH
DIRT
LIGHTNING
TACO
CRASH
MACK
CRUZ
ARVY
CRUNCH
MUDDY
RACERS
DOCTOR DAMAGE
DEMO

DEMOLITION DERBY

D	G	T	R	A	C	E	R	S	K	J	D	F
C	O	I	H	C	N	U	R	C	V	I	Q	P
L	U	C	C	R	A	S	H	K	R	I	A	H
N	H	P	T	L	C	N	U	T	R	K	V	B
W	O	L	L	O	H	R	E	D	N	U	H	T
H	F	J	G	G	R	X	U	T	L	S	M	J
V	J	U	J	X	N	D	A	S	L	V	A	O
T	A	C	O	C	L	I	A	U	H	D	C	M
Y	T	B	U	K	B	T	N	M	F	I	K	E
D	I	S	G	U	I	S	E	T	A	P	E	D
Z	H	Z	L	D	U	J	R	U	H	G	B	H
L	M	R	W	W	M	U	D	D	Y	G	E	J
I	Y	A	R	V	Y	C	R	U	Z	F	I	S
R	E	T	T	I	R	F	S	S	I	M	H	L

Unscramble the names of Lightning's biggest supporters.

T A M R E

___ ___ ___ ___ ___

L S A Y L

___ ___ ___ ___ ___

Z R C U I E Z R M A R

___ ___ ___ ___   ___ ___ ___ ___ ___ ___ ___

K O M E S Y

___ ___ ___ ___ ___ ___

nswer: Mater, Sally, Cruz Ramirez, Smokey

Cruz doesn't know what to do.

VROOM! Miss Fritter is hot on Lightning's tail!

Label each puzzle piece with the correct letter-number combination.

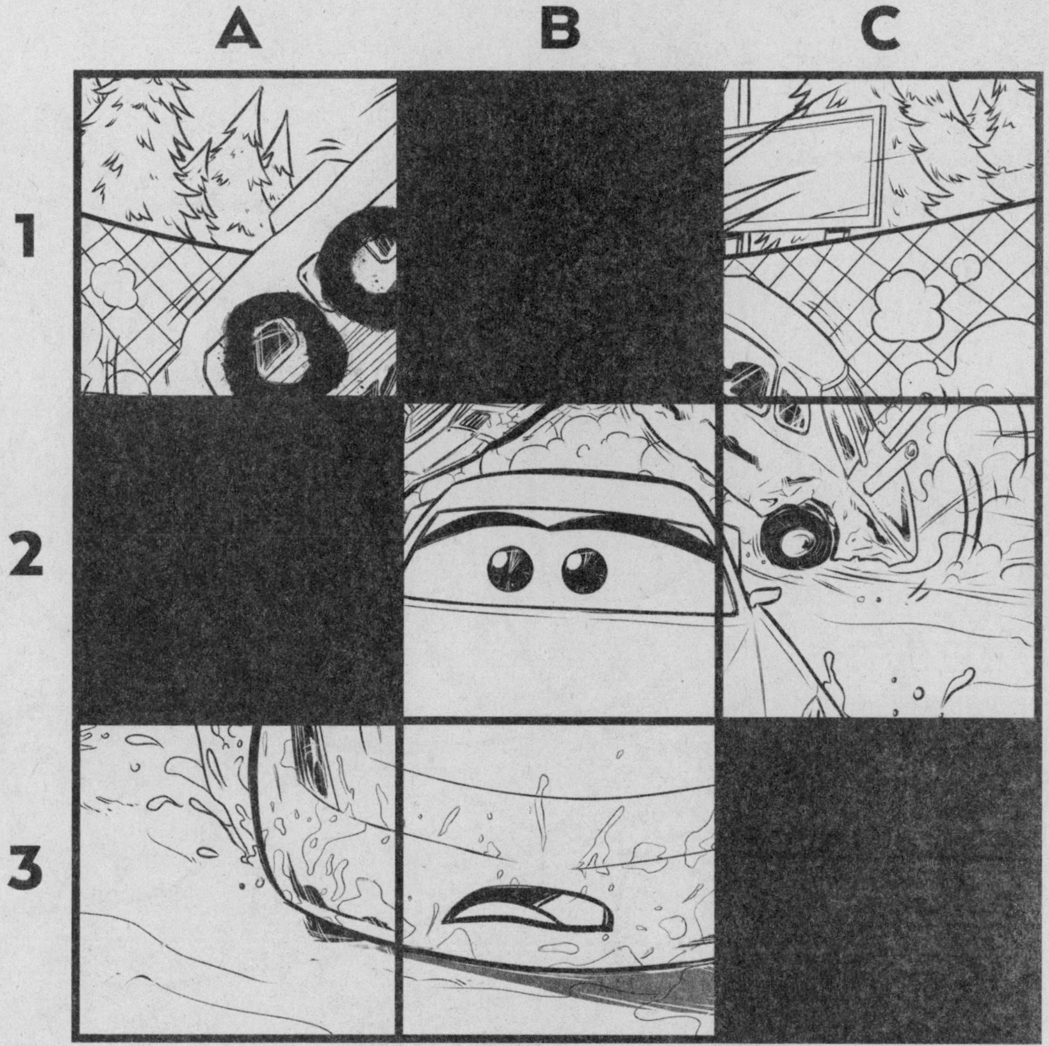

	A	B	C
1			
2			
3			

______ ______ ______

Answer: B-1, C-3, A-

Which line leads Lightning to Cruz Ramirez?
95
A
B
C
Your Answer:
46'S > 33 DEGREE BANK > .40 DR

Lightning and Cruz arrive at Doc's racetrack in Thomasville.

Lightning and Cruz take a lap around the Thomasville track.

Help Lightning figure out the correct order of the pieces of the mixed-up picture at the bottom of the page. Use the picture at the top of the page as a guide. Write the correct sequence of numbers in the spaces below the mixed-up picture.

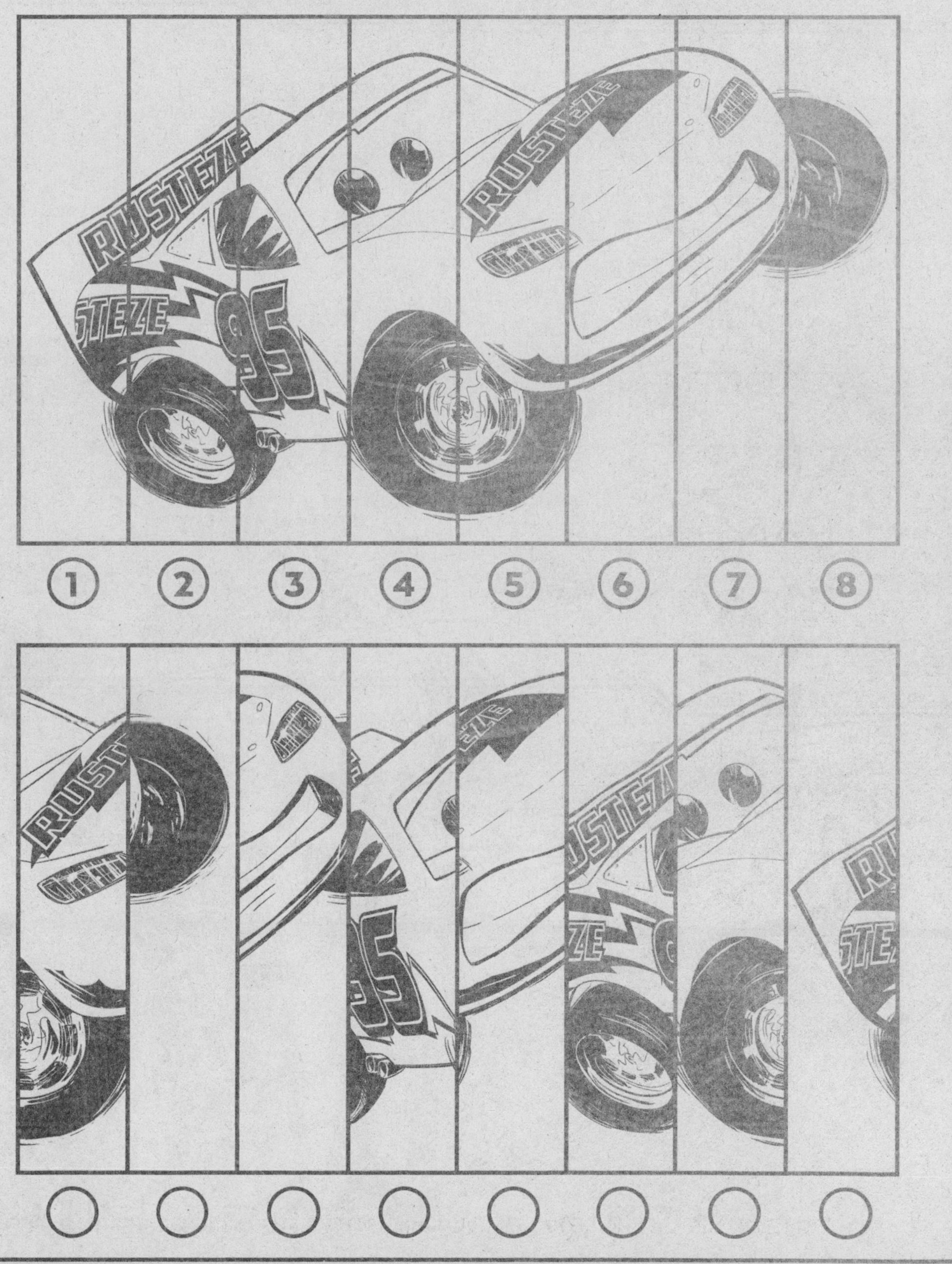

Answer: 5, 8, 7, 3, 6, 2, 4, 1

ON THE TRACK

VROOM
HUM
CLANK
ROAR
SCREECH
CRASH
BANG
ZOOM
BEEP
HISS
SQUEAL
WHOOSH
SPUTTER
CRANK
RUMBLE
BUZZ

ON THE TRACK

R Z W W R X L I B M D Z Z
O W H V Y E I M A R I B F
A R O R Z B T U N K E E Z
R W O O E E W T G U X E M
J E S O N L A B U Q U P N
R Q H M C Z B X K P O C G
B K U G H Z V M L S S R R
S H L Y R V S U U C C A Q
A Z I X C Y E V P R R N P
E U K F U L U Z Y A E K N
Z Z U B L E D N H S E O J
U L A E U Q S I M H C N Q
K N A L C V S O P D H F A
A A M K K S Q Z O O M W C

4G'S > 33 DEGREE BANK > .40 DR

Smokey used to be Doc Hudson's crew chief.

Use the grid to draw Smokey.

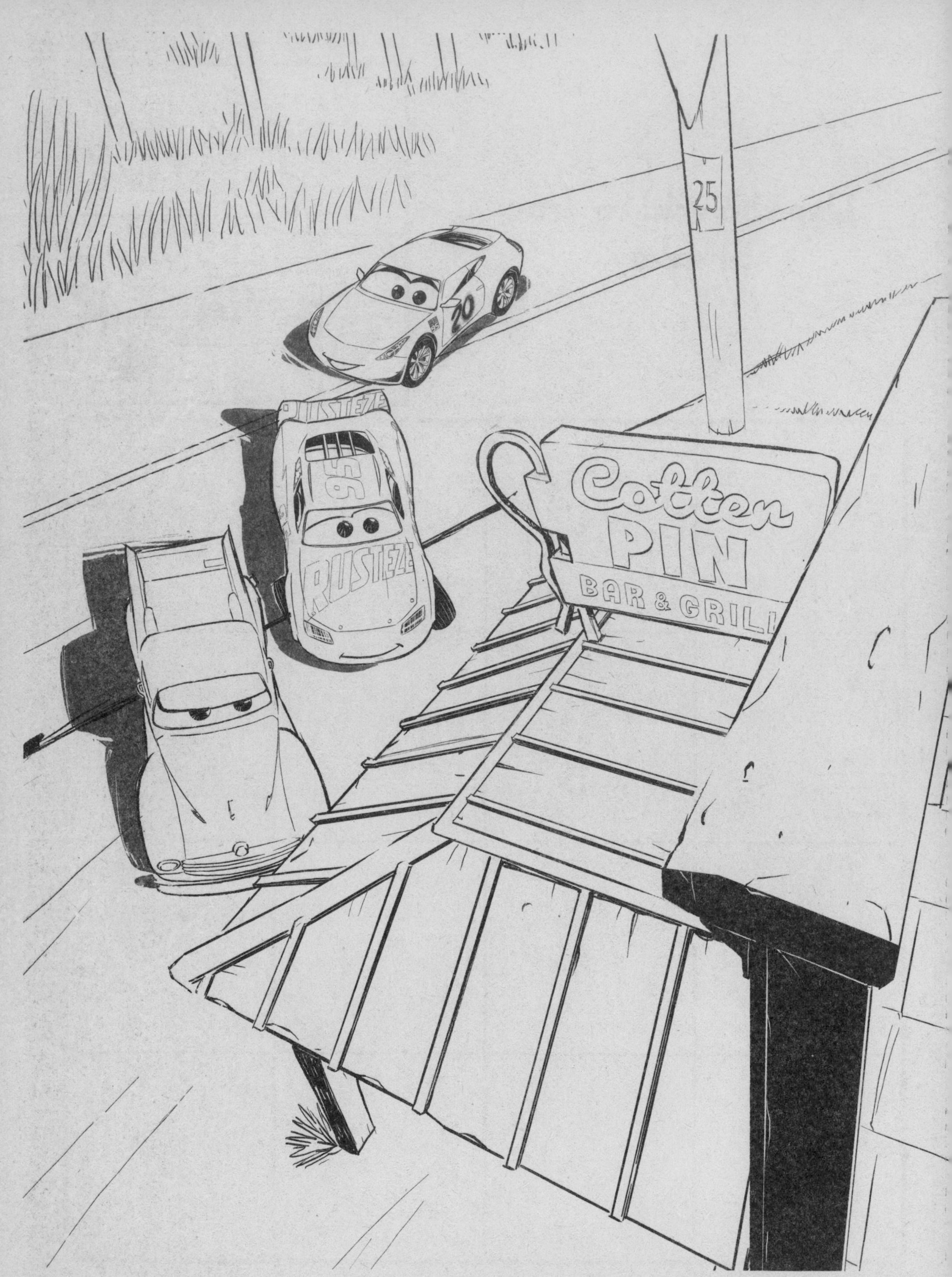

Smokey invites Lightning into the Cotter Pin
to meet some old friends.

Legendary racer, River Scott, used to race with Doc Hudson.

Louise Nash was known as the "First Lady of Racing".
She was a top racer in her day.

Junior Moon was a Piston Cup racer.
Doc Hudson learned a lot from him.

Match the character with their shadow.

4G'S > 33 DEGREE BANK > .40 DR

Answer: A-3, B-5, C-1, D-2, E-4

Cruz is thrilled to meet the Legends.

LET'S RACE

VELOCITY
THRILLS
FAST
FINISH
DYNAMIC
RIDE
VICTORY
RACING
NEXT-GEN
INTENSITY
SPEED
REV
MOMENTUM
DATA
THROTTLE
SUPERCHARGED

46'S > 33 DEGREE BANK > .40 DR

LET'S RACE

A E B C I M A N Y D S V W
L X I Y F J G U M P E Q V
D Y E M V F V U E L O A S
E T O D D X T E T L T X U
M T I R I N D T G O H Y P
N V D N E R O G N Y T Y E
E N I M T R N L I I S J R
X T O C H E E L C M A D C
T M H T T Q N O A D F F H
G A S R F O L S R V G M A
E T I H I E R V I N H C R
N A N N V L C Y E T G C G
X D I Y S W L C X R Y G E
R K F O W C M S H V I H D

4G'S > 33 DEGREE BANK > .40 DR

Long ago, Doc Hudson was one of the best racers around.